PiNKY and PEET

The Little Aussie Bush Lizards

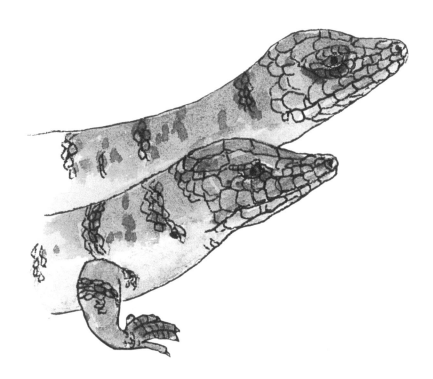

Written by Dawn Hawthorn-Jackson
Illustrated by Jan Finlayson

Pinky and Peet live in an
Aussie bush town.

One day, when they were not very old their mum climbed to the top of their burrow.

'Come and join me!' she said as she peeked outside.

'Wow, that's a long way up!' said Peet as he climbed to the top.

'I know,' said Pinky, huffing and puffing behind him.

Once outside Mum suggested
they wait for lunch.

In no time at all, Mum showed Pinky and Peet how to catch grasshoppers.

'Yum!' said Peet as he munched away.

Once their tummies were full, the curious lizards had many questions.

'Mum, why do we live in a spider burrow?' asked Pinky.

'Well, living in a spider burrow keeps us safe. And, because we can't build our own burrows, we need the spiders to build them for us,' explained Mum.

'Why don't the spiders live in the
burrows?' asked Peet.

Mum smiled. 'Sometimes they leave to
find a new home and sometimes they
get eaten by birds or other animals.'

'Ohh, I hope we don't get eaten,' cried Pinky.

'Well, we do have to be careful.
That's why it's best for us to sit by the
burrow. If we see or hear a bird or another
animal and feel a little scared, we can crawl
back down and feel safe,' cautioned Mum.

'Can animals get into our burrow?' asked Peet.

'Well, the hole is little like us so it's hard for bigger animals to get in, and we can safely curl up together at the bottom,' explained Mum.

Pinky yawned.

'Come on sleepy head, time to go back for a nap,' chuckled Mum.

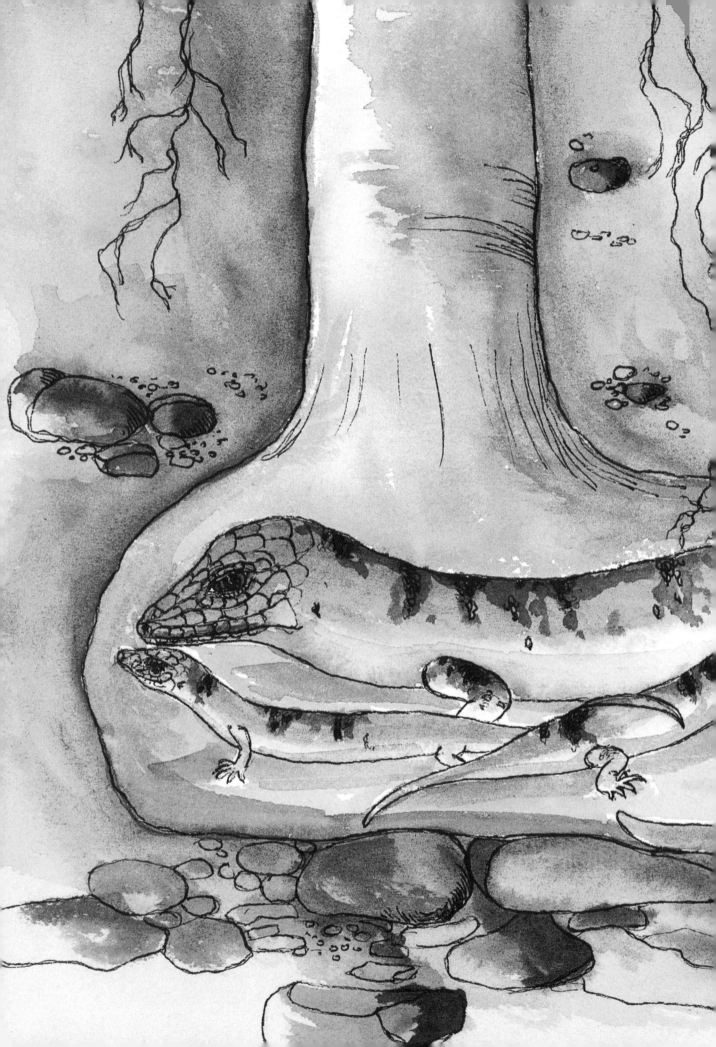

Back in the burrow, Mum
licked an insect off Peet's
head and then he and Pinky
settled down to have a nap.

But just when Mum thought that she too could have a rest, Pinky, with one eye open and one eye closed, looked at her and asked, 'Why do we have pink tongues?'

'Ahh my Little Pinky,' said Mum, 'because we are Pygmy Bluetongue Lizards.'

'But why aren't we Pygmy Pinktongue Lizards?' asked Peet.

'Hmm, let's talk about that another day,' laughed Mum as she curled up with her babies for an afternoon nap.

'Sweet dreams,' whispered Mum
as Pinky and Peet closed their eyes.

Shh! Can you see them sleeping?

Pygmy Bluetongue Lizard Facts

Pygmy Bluetongue Lizards were rediscovered near Burra, South Australia, Australia in 1992. Prior to this they had not been seen since the 1950's. Although over 20 populations are now known to live in the South Australian bush, they are still classified as endangered.

The Burra region is also known as Ngadjuri country.

Pygmy Bluetongue Lizards live in empty spider burrows. The burrows range in depth (from 10–75 cm), but are approximately 25 cm deep on average. The chamber at the bottom of the burrow gives the lizards room to easily move, turn around and curl up to sleep.

Pygmy Bluetongue Lizards sit at the entrance of their hole and wait for prey, which includes invertebrates such as spiders, grasshoppers, cockroaches and ants. They also eat a small amount of vegetation.

Predators of Pygmy Bluetongue Lizards like snakes and birds find it hard to get into the burrow.

Female Pygmy Bluetongue Lizards have their first litter when they are approximately 2 ½ years old. Litter size ranges from 1 to 4. The babies are about 5 cm long when born. They can grow to approximately 20 cm in length. The juveniles remain in the parental burrow for up to 12 weeks and then move out to find burrows of their own.

Pygmy Bluetongue Lizards have a pink tongue. They use their tongue to detect scents left by other lizards.

Pygmy Bluetongue populations can be adversely affected by the disturbance of native grassland ploughing, heavy grazing and the development of buildings, roads, and infrastructure. Climate change may also be a challenge for them. Research and conservation activities are helping to ensure their existence.

Pygmy Bluetongue Quiz

1. When were Pygmy Bluetongue Lizards rediscovered?

2. Where were Pygmy Bluetongue Lizards rediscovered?

3. Where do Pygmy Bluetongue Lizards live?

4. How deep is a Pygmy Bluetongue Lizard burrow?

5. How long are Pygmy Bluetongue Lizards when they are born?

6. How long is an adult Pygmy Bluetongue Lizard?

7. What colour tongue do Pygmy Bluetongue Lizards have?

8. What is a Pygmy Bluetongue Lizards tongue used for?

9. What do Pygmy Bluetongue Lizards eat?

10. What eats Pygmy Bluetongue Lizards?

With thanks to the Adelaide and Mount Lofty Ranges Natural Resources Management Board and Mike Bull at Flinders University for generous funding support.

To Riley, Joslyn, Emma, Gemma, Ed, Campbell, Georgia, Ailie, Rhyce and Eliza (Floey). May you never cease to wonder. *Aunty Dawn*

To Mike, for your dedication and commitment to your Pygmy Bluetongue research. *Jan*

Most of our understanding of the biology of this lizard has been developed with long-term funding from the Australian Research Council, and the Nature Foundation of South Australia.

Many researchers, project staff and volunteers have contributed to our knowledge of Pygmy Bluetongue Lizard biology and ecology. I thank you all for your contribution to this story. *Dawn*

Published by Emu Consulting
Email: emuconsulting111@gmail.com   Web: www.emuconsulting.com.au

Text © Dawn Hawthorn-Jackson
Illustrator © Jan Finlayson
Editor: Jan Finlayson

Publication design by Hardshell Publishing
Web: www.hardshellpublishing.com

First edition 2015
Second edition 2020

National Library of Australia Cataloguing-in-Publication entry

Creator:	Hawthorn-Jackson, Dawn, author.
Title:	Pinky and Peet : the little Aussie bush lizards / Dawn Hawthorn-Jackson ; Jan Finlayson.
Edition:	Second edition.
ISBN:	978-0-9942451-2-0 (paperback)
Target Audience:	For primary school age.
Subjects:	Lizards--Australia--Juvenile fiction.
Other Creators/Contributors:	
	Finlayson, Jan, illustrator.
Dewey Number:	A823.4

Government of South Australia
Adelaide and Mount Lofty Ranges
Natural Resources Management Board

Natural Resources
Adelaide and Mt Lofty Ranges

CPSIA information can be obtained
at www.ICGtesting.com
Printed in the USA
BVHW022023181120
593653BV00002B/6